Harper's Tail of Adventure

By John McLaughlin

For Kim and Harper,
the two loves of my life.

Harper's Tail of Adventure

ISBN: 978-0-6453791-0-5

Published by J. McLaughlin
First published in Australia 2022

A Catalogue-in-Publication (CiP) record for this book is available from the National Library of Australia.

Harper's Tail of Adventure

By John McLaughlin

Harper was excited. She and her brother Henry were off with their parents to spend a weekend in the country. She loved the different sounds and smells of the bush and couldn't wait to get there.

When they finally arrived in the country Harper **bounded** out of the car with glee.

She was always excited to explore new places and meet new friends.

The cows were very inquisitive and friendly.

'Who are youuu?'

they mooed.

'My name is Harper.'

'And what do you dooo?'

they mooed.

'I am an adventurer.'

Harper and Henry were playing in the field when Harper caught sight of a **kangaroo**. Harper loved to chase kangaroos and bounded after it.

'Don't go too far,'

called Henry.

It was Henry!

Harper was covered in kisses and hugs.
'I told you **not to go too far,**' he teased as Mum and Dad fretted and fussed over Harper's cuts and bruises.

Harper promised never to go off on an adventure by herself ever again.

Next time she will make
Henry come too!

Lightning Source UK Ltd.
Milton Keynes UK
UKRC032237270622
405052UK00001B/3

When she finally made her way out of the forest, Harper found herself at the side of a road.

She **barked** and **barked** as loud and long as she could.

She laid down **exhausted!**

Harper could go no further, and began to cry. Then she heard...

The platypus led Harper to a shallow part of the creek and showed her how to get across using **stepping** **stones** to reach the other side.

She followed the sound to a creek. The creek bubbled and frothed. It was too scary to cross... A platypus popped his head out of the water. 'I know how to get across.

Follow me.'

In the quiet of the morning
Harper watched the sun rise...

'Woof! Woof!'

It sounded like Henry, but far away on the other side of the creek.

That night, alone and scared of the night noises around her, Harper hid in a hollow log and fell asleep.

Meanwhile, Henry and her parents were frantically combing the countryside, calling for Harper to come home.

But Harper was too far away to hear.

Harper

Harper

Harper knew she was lost.

She was hungry, and her paws were sore.

She had never felt so **alone**.

out of the bushes

bounded

the kangaroo.

It wasn't Henry.

the very **middle** of the forest.

'Rustle.

Rustle.'

'Rustle. Rustle.'

Harper again pricked up her ears. 'Henry, is that you?'

It sounded like Henry, but the smell was different.

She followed it into...

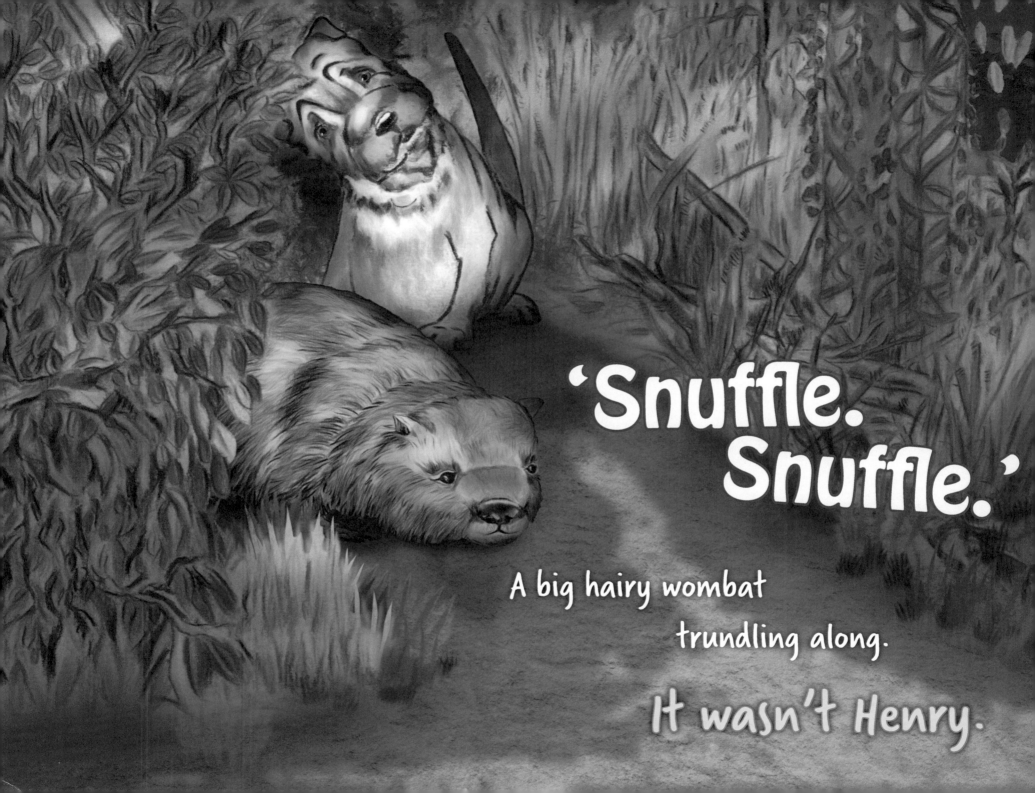

'Snuffle.
Snuffle.'

A big hairy wombat
trundling along.

It wasn't Henry.

'Snuffle. Snuffle.'

Harper pricked up her ears. 'Henry, is that you?'

It sounded like Henry, but the smell was different.

She followed it even deeper into the forest and found...

'Bark! Bark!'

Two dingo pups playing.

It wasn't Henry.

'Bark! Bark!'

Harper pricked up her ears. **'Henry, is that you?'**

It sounded like Henry, but the smell was different.

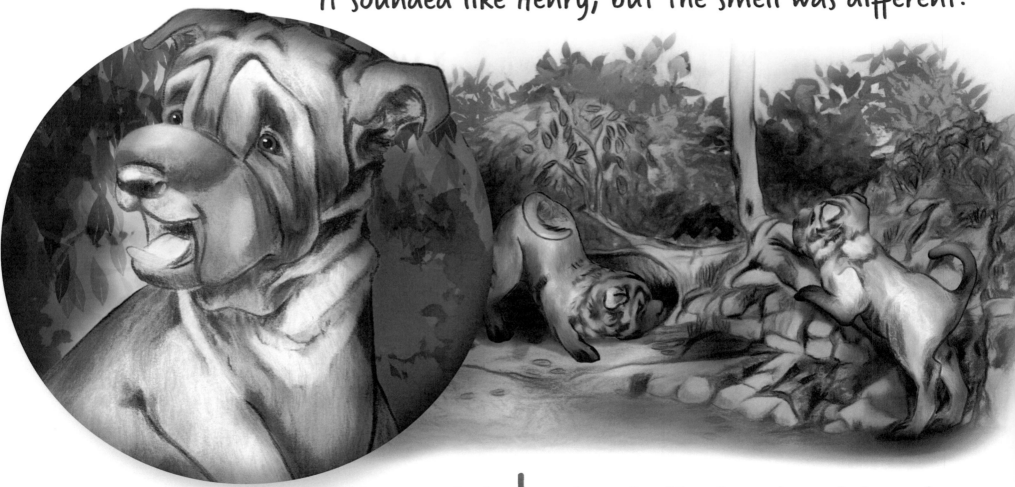

She followed it **deep** into the forest and found...

Hoot hoot

Harper looked up into the trees and saw a wise old owl.

'You shouldn't be here,'

said the wise old owl.

'I know,' replied Harper.

'I think I may be lost!'

The sun had set. The path was gone. What was Harper going to do?

Where was Henry? Was there anyone else around?

Deeper and deeper into the forest scampered Harper.

She couldn't see the kangaroo anymore. She couldn't see the campfire.

'It's late and you might get lost!'

But Harper was having way too much fun to listen

and left poor Henry

far

far

behind.